From Tammy Christmas 2009.